DREAMS AND WAKING VISIONS

M000168741

DREAMS AND WAKING VISIONS

A JOURNAL

Barbara Andrews and Mary Michael

ST. MARTIN'S PRESS / NEW YORK

DREAMS AND WAKING VISIONS: A JOURNAL. Copyright © 1989 by Barbara Andrews and Mary Michael. All rights reserved. Printed in the United States of America. No part of this book may be used or reproduced in any manner whatsoever without written permission except in the case of brief quotations embodied in critical articles or reviews. For information, address St. Martin's Press, 175 Fifth Avenue, New York, N.Y. 10010.

Design by Mary Michael
Cover design by Doris Borowsky
Front cover photograph by R. Michael Stuckey/COMSTOCK
Back cover photograph by Mark Helterline/COMSTOCK

Library of Congress Cataloging-in-Publication Data

Andrews, Barbara.
    Dreams and waking visions: a journal / Barbara Andrews and Mary Michael.
        p.   cm.
    "A Thomas Dunne book."
    ISBN 0-312-02907-1
    1. Dreams.   2. Symbolism (Psychology)   3. Dreams—Problems, exercises, etc.   4. Symbolism (Psychology)—Problems, exercises, etc.   I. Michael, Mary.   II. Title.
    BF1078.A58   1989
    154.6'34—dc19   89-30121
                                                              CIP

First Edition

10   9   8   7   6   5   4   3   2   1

The eye of man hath not heard,
the ear of man hath not seen,
man's hand is not able to taste,
his tongue to conceive, nor his heart report,
what my dream was.

—*William Shakespeare*, A Midsummer Night's Dream

TABLE OF CONTENTS

Dreams are the true interpreters of our inclinations;
but there is art required to sort and understand them.
—Michel de Montaigne

_____ _____   _____ _____
_____ _____   _____ _____
_____ _____   _____ _____
_____ _____   _____ _____
_____ _____   _____ _____
_____ _____   _____ _____
_____ _____   _____ _____
_____ _____   _____ _____
_____ _____   _____ _____
_____ _____   _____ _____
_____ _____   _____ _____
_____ _____   _____ _____
_____ _____
_____ _____
_____ _____
_____ _____

PART TWO

Personal Dream Symbols

INTRODUCTION

Dreams come to us as we sleep, a fantastic series of uncensored visions and ideas. They are as unique as the individual, as ancient as primordial life, more revolutionary and insightful than our conscious minds allow.

Dreams have been integral to the lives of people in diverse cultures from the beginning of time, helping humans to shape their understanding of themselves and Nature.

Primitive people considered dreams to be the key to a better sense of their own world. They also saw them as a link between themselves and the world of the gods, and for this reason made dreams the basis of much of their art and religions. Some believed that as they slept, these supernatural visions actually came to life on a very real but different level of being. The dreamer could intercommunicate with these images and the pure of spirit could secure their help in his or her own life. Others believed that the dreamer's spirit left the body while in a self-induced meditative dream state between the conscious and unconscious during which the dreamer could control and direct his or her own actions. (This state is similar to "lucid dreaming," a phenomenon claimed by many dreamers today.) Yet others envisioned wider, all-embracing dream states; the aboriginal people of Australia explain their very origin in the myths of the "dreamtime," stories that have been told and retold for over 10,000 years.

The ancient Egyptians were the first known culture to suspect that dreams contain "universal themes." They believed that dream images were representations of people, objects, and situations from waking reality and that their meanings and design were common to all people. Precise analyses of these abstractions were conducted by high priests, who viewed the strange and recurring symbols as hidden messages from the spirit world—messages that, if understood, could help man overcome hardship and illness, or be warned of impending danger. Eventually, as interpretations evolved they were recorded on papyrus and became the first "dream books."

At this time two prevailing dream theories emerged. In the first the entire dream was viewed as a metaphor for real events: events that were taking place, or would take place in the future. The second theory saw each individual image within a dream as a symbol for something else, a "dream symbol." In either case, the dream had a profound influence on daily life, and dream prophets were held in high regard. They were the protectors of a society's well-being, people who could make sense out of the vivid and sometimes disturbing dream imagination.

The Greek culture inherited many dream theories from the Egyptians. In the eighth century B.C., this influence played a central role in both *The Iliad* and *The Odyssey.* Eventually, however, Greek thinking began to gravitate toward the healing aspects of dream work. Dream physicians sought to cure the dreamer of ailments revealed by the symbols within dreams. The Greeks were innovative with this more personal approach to interpretation and were the first to recognize the astounding phenomenon of extrasensory perception during dreams.

In the second century A.D. the Roman Astrampsychus culled all the written and theoretical information available to him and created a series of five volumes called *Interpretation of Dreams.* This work became and remained the most extensive and important reference on the subject until the beginning of the present century, and it is still used as the basis for many current

I am conscious of having, in my sleep, transcended the limits of the individual.

Henry David Thoreau

books on dream language. Although his interpretations of dream metaphors were quite specific—"to creep up a mountain signifies the difficulty of business"—Astrampsychus also recognized that the meanings of dreams and the symbols they contained could vary with the individual. He also concluded that economic and social conditions, the dreamer's health, and recent events from the individual's life would affect the dream itself.

It was not until 1900, when Sigmund Freud published his own *Interpretation of Dreams,* that there was any significant advance in dream philosophy. Freud propounded the revolutionary new concept that dreams, "the royal road to the unconscious," are an expression of desires repressed during our waking life. The rising acceptance of his psychoanalytic theories gave contemporary dream study a more practical significance.

Following Freud, many other schools of thought have emerged and continue to evolve. C. G. Jung believed dreams to be the path to self-actualization: our striving to create a balance and restore harmony to our lives. Frederich Perls, the father of Gestalt, thought that all dream images contain parts of the dreamer's own personality and that we are the sum of the characters that live within us all. Alfred Adler wrote that dreams have a future orientation to them. He suggested that they arise out of life's unfinished business and support and reaffirm the dreamer's waking choices.

Today the interpretation of dreams need not be limited by ancient beliefs or even differing contemporary views. Through a personal interest in our own dreams we can strive to create a balance between the secular world and the spirituality that guides us on the quest for self-knowledge. And to aid in that search,

dreams tell us the truth about who we really are. They try to communicate with us whether we choose to listen or not. The ancients considered dreams the shape of their future. Who is to say that our attitudes and responses to waking life today and tomorrow are not continually affected and altered by unconscious decisions of the night?

As we have seen, many different theories attempt to explain the purpose and meaning behind dreams. There are countless books and lectures that explain and teach new methods and concepts of dream reading. But regardless of one's philosophical orientation, there is one aspect of dream study upon which scientists, spiritualists, psychologists, and dream therapists agree, and that is the value and importance in keeping a dream journal. The significance of a dream inspires it, its fragile nature demands it, and one can only learn to read what has been written.

PART I: Journal of Significant Dreams

During the day we experience a barrage of external stimuli that affect our physical and emotional lives but is far too diffuse to absorb consciously. Dreams process these happenings. They explore our incredible resources in an attempt to reach some solution to problems and difficulties that arise. They are vivid expressions of our conception of self and provide a wonderful way of articulating a variety of emotions and feelings and relating them both to our remembered past and to our hopes and fears of the future. The demands of life may steal one's time for waking contemplation, but dreams are there to create a balance between stark reality and the great unconscious world of possibilities and universal truth.

Unfortunately dreams are fleeting images, lost far more easily than our waking memories. So if you wish to gain the wisdom and understanding about yourself that is possible through the study and interpretation of dreams, you must first remember them.

Surprisingly, dream recall is a learned ability. Those who claim that they rarely dream during the night have probably not made a conscious effort to call up their dreams in the morning. A lack of commitment, as well as stress or fears, can have a negative effect on your ability to remember a night vision. In these cases it will help to remind yourself before falling asleep each evening that you *will* remember your dreams. Program yourself, if necessary, to awaken as soon as your dream is finished. Most people know that they dream and can recount instances from particularly bizarre or emotionally charged dreams. Eventually, though, without a way to record them, even these will become unclear and all will fade from memory.

Writing down a dream as soon as possible upon awakening cultivates a discipline that will quickly improve your overall ability to recall dreams. Soon even tiny fragments can be saved. These pieces will begin to shape a permanent and useful record to reread and study — a detailed dream history that becomes a wonderful gift to oneself and a great opportunity for enlightenment.

KEEPING YOUR DREAM JOURNAL

Dream journals are for preserving the personal memoirs of the night. Unlike a daily diary or notebook, they provide a convenient medium specifically designed to record dream narrative. In this journal, you will find space for essential notes, interpretation, themes, character and image sketches, and a place to number and date each dream. There is also a special section in which to list personal dream symbols once the dreamer has become more familiar with his or her own dream language.

The journal's major portion is given over to space for narrative and interpretation. Some dreams are short and may require only a few lines of one page, but other more significant ones may be quite involved, especially as visions become more vivid. Continue your narrative over onto the next page if necessary.

It is imperative that you write down at least a short synopsis of a dream as soon as possible upon waking. (A tape recorder is also useful for this purpose.) These notes will help later in pulling additional details from the edge of memory for the final

A dream is a theatre in which the dreamer is himself the scene, the player, the prompter, the producer, the author, the public, and the critic.

—C. G. Jung

transcription. But do not wait too long before writing down the full dream sequence, as there is a tendency to "edit" dreams with time.

The longest and most memorable dreams often occur just prior to waking in the morning, so this is the dream most often recorded. You may prefer to record only these or only your most special dreams at first. But as your proficiency in recall and writing improves and becomes less time-consuming, it is beneficial to record dream series from the entire night. You may discover that the separate episodes are somehow related, pieces of an integrated whole. Seemingly insignificant remnants may be appreciated later.

DREAM INTERPRETATION

As it develops, your dream journal will be fascinating. Contained within its pages will be the seeds of self-discovery — information that can help resolve a conflict or reveal hidden talents and creative energy. But to obtain this knowledge the dreamer must learn to interpret what has been recorded. You might find it helpful to read books on dreams, myths, and symbolism to open up new insights and enrich your understanding of the subject. A dream therapist or psychologist can also be helpful if needed or desired, but it is the dreamer who is most qualified to discover her or his own dream language. Only *you* possess the knowledge, personal history, and feelings that are the key to interpretation.

First, every dream has an overall focus or theme: "escaping through a black hole or tunnel into nothingness," "meeting myself on a long path," etc. Make a note of this theme and use it as a title for the dream. In the future you may begin to recognize recurring themes and patterns, perhaps arising from some troubling situation that continues to erupt periodically. It is not uncommon to have repetitive dreams. They will most likely continue until life experience has come to terms with the issue or the problem. The Table of Contents has space to list your titles (themes) and dream numbers. This easy referral system will facilitate a search back to former dreams.

This journal provides space for recording dream meanings. There is a ruled column on the right-hand page, on which the dreamer can record notes. It is important to list any events or instances from life that may have affected the dream: the stage of life, events in our past, and the thoughts that ruled the mind immediately preceding falling asleep. Always focus on the emotions that came into play. They may be the key to interpretation. And be sure never to try to force a meaning onto a dream that is not there. Real revelations may surface weeks or even months later, and you can then go back and record these insights as they occur.

PERSONAL DREAM SYMBOLS

The language of dreams is a picture language, a series of hieroglyphs; communication, if we achieve it, is through imagery. It is a very primitive language that goes back to the dawn of man but can be a far more efficient way of imparting information than

the spoken word. It allows the sleeping mind to condense many different ideas and impressions into one consolidated image.

Although the primary mode while dreaming is perceptual, we can learn to translate this imagistic language to the conceptual. At times this is easy; dreams can express our feelings quite literally. They deal with characters or images from our current waking life. We immediately recognize who or what they are, even though the dream may express a desire or emotion of which we are not consciously aware.

Most dreams, however, translate thoughts to pictures, using visual metaphors in the same way that we use verbal metaphors—"a dog's life," "high as a kite," "climbing up the corporate ladder"—to give emotional impact to our words. In a dream these images can appear as puns, visions from our past, or humorous or even frightening representations of the people, situations, emotions, and relationships within our world.

But what specifically do each of these symbols represent? How do we learn to decipher them? Are there universal meanings behind the images? What are these animals, these aliens, these bridges or mountains or oceans trying to tell me? What does it mean when I fly? And why do some of these elements appear over and over again? Quite often these pictures do not seem to represent anything even remotely familiar.

Freud, as we know, believed that dreams revealed certain aspects of our behavior that were denied or repressed in our waking life. He also felt that because our censoring conscious mind is not totally restrained while dreaming and would resist true interpretation of unpleasant truths, we express our "forbidden" desires indirectly, as symbols. He also believed that

the symbolism that emerged in dreams was common to all mankind.

Today it is commonly accepted that the symbols contained in dreams reveal rather than conceal the truth and are more personal in nature than formerly believed. They spring forth from the limitless repertoire of metaphorical and social images, from slang that is common to our individual culture, and from the uniqueness of our individual experience. We choose symbols that hold personal meaning for us and use them quite creatively in context within the dream to express our feelings in a complex and exaggerated manner. Objects or images can represent anything or anyone, including our state of mind and our own self-image, or may represent specific problems in our lives. They can appear repeatedly throughout our dream life as some significance has been attached to them; meaning and symbolism can shift and change throughout our life as we adopt or believe the symbols of others. This is why many images may seem to have "universal" interpretations. The lion, for example, represents strength and nobility to many differing peoples because these are common attributes associated with the animal and appear as such within many dreams. A pig, however, might prove to hold a very different meaning in the dreams of a feminist than in those of a farmer, whose livelihood depends on the animal. Much depends on the feeling that the symbol conveys during the dream or on a person's memories and experiences regarding it.

To fully understand your dreams it is important to learn the vocabulary of your personal dream language. Examine each image or character soon after it has been recorded in your dream journal and relate it to your own life experiences. Ask yourself "What did

I feel?" "Is there anything happening in my life recently that reminds me of this image?" "Does the name of the image relate to the name of something familiar?" "What was I thinking about prior to falling asleep?" Once a relationship begins to emerge and has the ring of truth to it, you should record the information in the back section of the book entitled Personal Dream Symbols. As you record and study your dreams on a regular basis, you will soon learn to label these mythic structures of the imagination and develop an intellectual understanding of what the images represent. They are the key to dream comprehension. Keeping a personal dictionary or glossary of dream symbols is an advanced technique that develops over time and will provide the greatest rewards in understanding.

SKETCHING DREAM IMAGES

Finally, there is a box on the left-hand page of your dream journal for sketching dream landscapes or symbols. This exercise can be done in the form of a written description or as a drawing. Even if you are not artistically inclined you can benefit from some kind of rough sketch of characters or objects that stand out as important elements in your dream. If you do not feel comfortable drawing, use the space to write a more detailed description of these important figures — including yourself as you have been portrayed in the dream. Often, taking the extra time to illustrate will allow the dreamer immediately to attach a meaning or persona to the image. As dream recording progresses over time, these evolving forms, from self to lovers and others in one's waking life, reincarnate again and again within the journal. They can add a new dimension to the richness, humor, and creativity of your dream life.

Dream No. _____

Date _____

Dream Sketch _____

I slept and dreamed that life was beauty.
I woke—and found that life was duty.
—Ellen Surgis Hooper
Beauty and Duty

_____

_____

_____

_____

_____

_____

_____

_____

_____

_____

_____

_____

_____

_____

_____

_____

_____

_____

_____

_____

Notes _____

_____

_____

_____

_____

_____

_____

_____

_____

_____

_____

_____

_____

_____

_____

_____

_____

_____

D ream No. _____

Date _____

Dream Sketch _____

And one day there will come a great awakening,
when we shall realize that life itself was a great dream.
—Chuang-Tzu, 350 B.C.

Notes

Dream No. _____

Date _____

Dream Sketch _____

I would rather think of life as a good book. The further you get into it, the more it begins to come together and make sense.

—Rabbi Harold Kushner,
When Everything You've Ever Wanted
Isn't Enough, *1988*

Notes

Dream No. _____

Date _____

Dream Sketch _____

I do not believe that I am now dreaming, but I cannot prove I am not.

—Bertrand Russell

Notes

Dream No. _____

Date _____

Dream Sketch _____

Both dreams and myths are important communications from ourselves to ourselves.
—Erich Fromm

_____

Notes _____

Dream No. _____

Date _____

Dream Sketch _____

Our truest life is when we are in dreams awake.
—Henry David Thoreau

Notes

Dream No. _____

Date _____

Drem Sketch _____

A dream which is not understood is like a letter which is not opened.

—The Talmud

Notes _____

Dream No. _____

Date _____

Dream Sketch _____

Dreams have a poetic integrity and truth.
—Ralph Waldo Emerson

Notes

Dream No. _____

Date _____

Dream Sketch _____

Deep in the night/down in my dreams
Glorious sight/this soul has seen

—James Taylor

Notes

Dream No. _____

Date _____

Dream Sketch _____

It may be those that do most, dream most.
—Stephen Leacock

Notes

Dream No. _____

Date _____

Dream Sketch _____

You must have chaos in your heart to give birth to a dancing star.

—Friedrich Nietzsche

Notes

Dream No. _____

Date _____

Dream Sketch _____

Dreams are necessary to Life.
—Anaïs Nin

Notes

Dream No. _____

Date _____

Dream Sketch _____

Are we then God's dream set to music in the place where the sea and the wind have begun to awake and think?

—Guy Murchie, *Seven Mysteries of Life*

_____

Notes _____

Dream No. _____

Date _____

Dream Sketch _____

When we are asleep, we awake to another form of existence. We dream.

—Erich Fromm

Notes

Dream No. _____

Date _____

Dream Sketch _____

My dreams are not me; they are not Nature, or the Not-me; they are both.

—Ralph Waldo Emerson

Notes

Dream No. _____

Date _____

Dream Sketch _____

Man is a microcosm of the universe; therefore what man is, is a clue to the universe.

—David Bohm

Notes

Dream No. _____

Date _____

Dream Sketch _____

If you have built castles in the air, your work need not be lost; there is where they should be. Now put foundations under them.

—Henry David Thoreau

Notes _____

Dream No. _____

Date _____

Dream Sketch _____

Our chief goal is a kind of self-knowledge as deep as our oldest myth; how it came about on this earth that the quick were first departed from the dead.

—*Philip Morrison*

Notes

Dream No.

Date

Dream Sketch

*Eyes illuminate the sleeping brain, but in the
daylight man's future cannot be seen.*
—*Aeschylus*, Eumenides

Notes _____

Dream No. _____

Date _____

Dream Sketch _____

The inquiry into a dream is another dream.
—Lord Halifax

Notes

43

Dream No. _____

Date _____

Dream Sketch _____

Dreams are the best evidence that we are not as firmly shut in our skins as it seems.

—*Friedrich Hebbel*

Notes

Dream No. _____

Date _____

Dream Sketch _____

You see things and say "Why?" But I dream things that never were; and I say "Why not?"
—George Bernard Shaw

Notes

Dream No. _____

Date _____

Dream Sketch _____

These whimsical pictures, inasmuch as they originate from us, may well have any analogy with our whole life and fate.

—Goethe

Notes _____

Dream No. _____

Date _____

Dream Sketch _____

Those things that have occupied a man's thoughts and affections while awake recur to his imagination while asleep.

—Thomas Aquinas

Notes _____

Dream No. _____

Date _____

Dream Sketch _____

*Sleep takes off the costume of circumstance, arms us
with terrible freedom, so that every will rushes to a deed.*
—Ralph Waldo Emerson

Notes

D ream No. _____

Date _____

Dream Sketch _____

Vodka gives one marvellous dreams I have discovered, but prevents one from sleeping. Every night lately I have dreamed luxuriously but slept ill.
—Evelyn Waugh

Notes

Dream No. _____

Date _____

Dream Sketch _____

If there were dreams to sell,
Merry and sad to tell,
And the crier rung his bell,
What would you buy?

—*Thomas Lovell Beddoes*

Notes

Dream No. _____

Date _____

Dream Sketch _____

When the will is yet wholly asleep the mind works like a machine without friction.

—Henry David Thoreau

Notes

Dream No. _____

Date _____

Dream Sketch _____

Dreams in their development have breath,
And tears, and tortures, and the touch of joy . . .
—Byron

Notes

Dream No. _____

Date _____

Dream Sketch _____

That holy dream—that holy dream,
While all the world were chiding,
Hath cheered me as a lovely beam
A lonely spirit guiding

—Edgar Allan Poe

Notes

Dream No. _____

Date _____

Dream Sketch _____

Dream, dream, dream . . . .
—Everly Brothers, song by Boudleaux Bryant

Notes

Dream No. _____

Date _____

Dream Sketch _____

It's a garden of wisdom from some long ago dream.
—Carole King

Notes

Dream No. _____

Date _____

Dream Sketch _____

*Bid your soul travel to any land you choose and
sooner than you bid it go, it will be there.*
Hermes Trismegistus

Notes

Dream No. _____

Date _____

Dream Sketch _____

Dreams surely are for the spirit what sleep is for the body.

—*Friedrich Hebbel*

Notes

71

Dream No. _____

Date _____

Dream Sketch _____

An artist is a dreamer consenting to dream of the actual world.

—George Santayana

Notes

Dream No. _____

Date _____

Dream Sketch _____

The waking have one common world, but the sleeping turn aside each into a world of his own.
—Heraclitus

Notes

Dream No. _____

Date _____

Dream Sketch _____

The fact will one day flower into a truth.
—Henry David Thoreau

Notes _____

Dream No. _____

Date _____

Dream Sketch _____

The essential thing is not to find, but to absorb what we find.

—Paul Valéry

Notes

Dream No. _____

Date _____

Dream Sketch _____

No man can reveal to you aught but that which
already lies half asleep in the dawning of your knowledge.
—Kahlil Gibran

Notes

Dream No. _____

Date _____

Dream Sketch _____

Method is the mother of memory.
—Thomas Fuller

Notes _____

Dream No. _____

Date _____

Dream Sketch _____

I like the dreams of the future better than the history of the past.

—*Thomas Jefferson*

Notes

Dream No. _____

Date _____

Dream Sketch _____

Even sleepers are workers and collaborators in what goes on in the universe.

—Heraclitus

Notes

Dream No. _____

Date _____

Dream Sketch _____

Normally we do not so much look at things as overlook them.

—Allan Watts

Notes _____

Dream No. _____

Date _____

Dream Sketch _____

Sanity is a madness put to good uses; waking life is a dream controlled.

—George Santayana

Notes

ream No. _____

Date _____

Dream Sketch _____

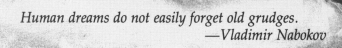

Human dreams do not easily forget old grudges.
—Vladimir Nabokov

Notes _____

Dream No. _____

Date _____

Dream Sketch _____

All days are nights to see till I see thee,
And nights bright days when dreams do show thee me.
—William Shakespeare

Notes

Dream No. _____

Date _____

Dream Sketch _____

Dreams are merciless; they come upon you when you're asleep.

—Joseph Heller

Notes

Dream No. _____

Date _____

Dream Sketch _____

There is a divination concerning some things in dreams not incredible.

—*Aristotle*

Notes _____

Dream No. _____

Date _____

Dream Sketch _____

I dreamt I dwelt in marble halls,
And each damp thing that creeps and crawls
Went wobble-wobble on the walls.
—Lewis Carroll

Notes

Dream No. _____

Date _____

Dream Sketch _____

All dreams of the soul
End in a beautiful man's or woman's body.

—W. B. Yeats

Notes

Dream No. _____

Date _____

Dream Sketch _____

Learn from your dreams what you lack.
—W. H. Auden

Notes

D ream No. _____

Date _____

Dream Sketch _____

I want to keep my dreams, even bad ones, because without them, I might have nothing all night long.
—Joseph Heller

Notes

Dream No. _____

Date _____

Dream Sketch _____

Dreams are rudiments of the great state to come. We dream what is about to happen.

—Bailey

Notes

Dream No. _____

Date _____

Dream Sketch _____

By lessons some are enlightened,
By sleep others are inspired.
—*Sibylline Oracles*

_____
_____
_____
_____
_____
_____
_____
_____
_____
_____
_____
_____
_____
_____
_____
_____
_____
_____
_____
_____

Notes _____
_____
_____
_____
_____
_____
_____
_____
_____
_____
_____
_____
_____
_____
_____
_____
_____
_____

Dream No. _____

Date _____

Dream Sketch _____

What we need is a myth of our own.

—C. G. Jung

Notes _____

Dream No. _____

Date _____

Dream Sketch _____

We are such stuff as dreams are made on, and our little life is rounded with a sleep.
—William Shakespeare, The Tempest

Notes

D ream No. _____

Date _____

Dream Sketch _____

Is this a dream? Oh! if it be a dream
Let me sleep on, and do not wake me yet.

—Longfellow

Notes

Dream No. _____

Date _____

Dream Sketch _____

Dreams are true while they last, and do we not live in dreams?

—*Tennyson*

Notes

D ream No. _____

Date _____

Dream Sketch _____

Any accumulation of minute details however silly it may appear is the only correct means to reach fundamental truths.

—A. F. Bandelier

Notes

Dream No. _____

Date _____

Dream Sketch _____

Just as true humor is laughter at oneself, true humanity is knowledge of oneself.

—*Alan Watts*

Dream No. _____

Date _____

Dream Sketch _____

I have had a most rare vision. I have had a dream,
past the wit of man to say what dream it was. . . .
—William Shakespeare,
A Midsummer Night's Dream

_____

Notes _____

Dream No. _____

Date _____

Dream Sketch _____

The most skillful interpreter of dreams is he who has the faculty of observing resemblances.

—Aristotle

Notes

Dream No. _____

Date _____

Dream Sketch _____

It shall be called "Bottom's Dreams," because it hath no bottom; and I will sing it in the latter end of a play.
—William Shakespeare,
A Midsummer Night's Dream

Notes

Dream No. _____

Date _____

Dream Sketch _____

They pique us by independence of us, yet we know ourselves in this mad crowd, and owe to dreams a kind of divination and wisdom.

—*Ralph Waldo Emerson*

_____

_____

_____

_____

_____

_____

_____

_____

_____

_____

_____

_____

_____

_____

_____

_____

_____

_____

Notes _____

_____

_____

_____

_____

_____

_____

_____

_____

_____

_____

_____

_____

_____

_____

_____

Dream No. _____

Date _____

Dream Sketch _____

Everything you do in a dream has a purpose, beyond your understanding while you are asleep.
—Kilton Stewart

Notes _____